primer
level

FAVORITE
CLASSIC MELODIES

Arranged
by

JAMES
BASTIEN

KJOS WEST • Neil A. Kjos Music Company, Publisher • San Diego, California

PREFACE

Favorite Classic Melodies (Primer Level through Level 4) provides a source of learning and enjoyment representing the major works for the symphony, opera, chorus, and piano. These books may be used in conjunction with any piano course for supplementary enrichment.

Suggested Use of Materials with "PIANO LESSONS, Primer Level"

At the **first lesson** the student may be given . . . . **Music Notebook** (GP16)
After completing **page 6,** the student is ready to begin . . . . **Theory Lessons**—Primer Level (WP6)
After completing **page 13,** the student is ready to begin . . . . **Technic Lessons**—Primer Level (WP11)
After completing **page 25,** the student is ready to begin . . . . **Piano Solos**—Primer Level (WP22)
After completing **page 33,** the student is ready to begin . . . . **Music Flashcards** (GP27)
After completing **page 56,** the student is ready to begin
    these Supplementary Books . . . . **Christmas Favorites**—Primer Level (WP48)
                                       Favorite Classic Melodies—Primer Level (WP72)
                                       Folk Tune Favorites—Primer Level (WP46)
                                       Hymn Favorites—Primer Level (WP43)
                                       Piano Recital Solos—Primer Level (WP64)

SHEET MUSIC from **Primer Level Solos** may be assigned to the student at the teacher's discretion. (Begin sheet music with Unit 6.)

ISBN 0-8497-5127-6

Published by Kjos West.
Distributed by Neil A. Kjos Music Company.
National Order Desk, 4382 Jutland Dr., San Diego, CA 92117

CONTENTS

Duet Accompaniment

Can Can

from the opera "Orpheus in the Underworld"

Jacques Offenbach
arr. by James Bastien

When used as a duet, play one octave higher.

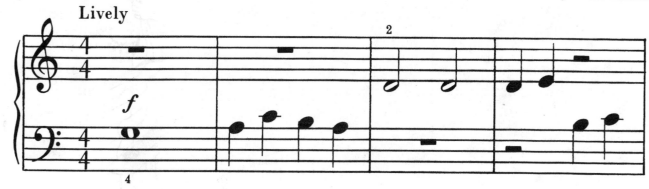

Liebestraum
(Dream of Love)

Franz Liszt
arr. by James Bastien

Slumber Song

from the opera "Hansel and Gretel"

Engelbert Humperdinck
arr. by James Bastien

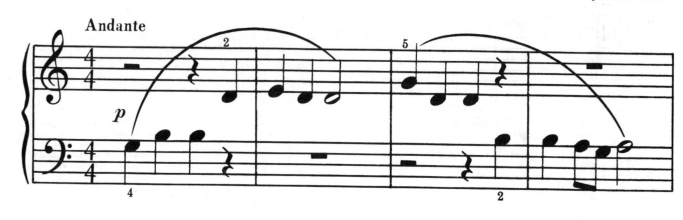

Symphony No. 1
Theme

Johannes Brahms
arr. by James Bastien

Merry Widow Waltz
from the operetta "The Merry Widow"

When used as a duet, play one octave higher.

Franz Lehar
arr. by James Bastien

Etude Theme

Frédéric Chopin
arr. by James Bastien

When used as a duet, play one octave higher.

Duet Accompaniment

William Tell Overture

Theme

Gioacchino Rossini
arr. by James Bastien

With spirit

Egyptian Dance
from the opera "Samson and Delilah"

Camille Saint-Saëns
arr. by James Bastien

Minuet in G

Johann Sebastian Bach
arr. by James Bastien

When used as a duet, play one octave higher.

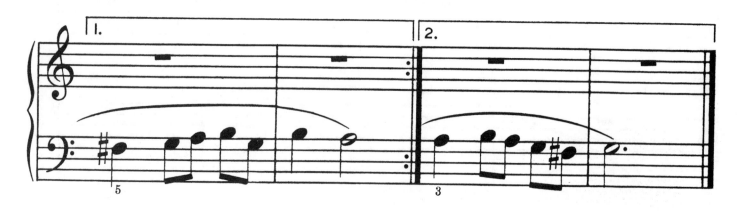

Surprise Symphony
Theme

Joseph Haydn
arr. by James Bastien

Turkish March
from "Ruins of Athens"

Ludwig van Beethoven
arr. by James Bastien

March tempo

Duet Accompaniment

Fantasie-Impromptu

Frédéric Chopin
arr. by James Bastien

Bridal Chorus
from the opera "Lohengrin"

Richard Wagner
arr. by James Bastien

March tempo

Students may play ♩. ♪ "by ear," or by counting with numbers, or by saying note values: ♩. ♪
quarter dot eighth.

On Wings of Song

Felix Mendelssohn
arr. by James Bastien

Moderato

23

WP72

Melody

Anton Rubinstein
arr. by James Bastien